Tips for Reading Together

Children learn best when reading is fun.

- Talk about the title and the pictures on the cover.
- Discuss what you think the story might be about.
- Read the story together, inviting your child to read with you.
- Give lots of praise as your child reads with you, and help them when necessary.
- Try different ways of helping if they get stuck on a word. For example: read the first sound or syllable of the word, read the whole sentence, or refer to the picture. Focus on the meaning.
- Have fun finding the hidden dragonflies, frogs, fish and newts.
- Re-read the story later, encouraging your child to read as much of it as they can.

Children enjoy re-reading stories and this helps to build their confidence.

Have fun!

Find the 3 dragonflies, 3 frogs, 3 fish and 3 newts hidden in the pictures.

The Raft Race

Roderick Hunt • Alex Brychta

OXFORD

UNIVERSITY PRESS

The children were at the river.

It was raft race day.

Mum and Dad made a raft.

The children helped.

"It's a good raft," said Dad.
"Let's get it into the water."

They slid the raft into the water.
Dad pulled it. Wilma and Chip
pushed.

Mum and Dad got on.

"Don't fall in," said Wilf.

The raft race started. Mum and
Dad went fast.

"Go! Go! Go!" shouted Biff.

"You can win."

Mum and Dad went faster.
"Come on!" panted Dad. "We
can win."

Oh no! The raft broke in half.
SPLASH! Dad fell in the water.

"Go on, Mum," shouted Wilf.
"You can still win."

Mum kept going.

Dad got back on his raft.

"Go on, Dad," shouted Wilma.

"Go as fast as you can."

Oh no! The raft broke again.
SPLASH! Dad fell in the water.

Mum kept going and she
won the race!

"Good old Mum," said Wilma.

"Poor old Dad," said Wilf.

Think about the story

Why did the raft break in half?

What did Dad do after the raft broke?

The children were pleased for Mum. How did they feel about Dad?

Have you ever been in a boat or on a raft? What would you do if you fell in?

Find the pairs

Each set of creatures has an odd one out.
Can you find each one?

More books for you to enjoy

Level 1:
Getting Ready

Level 2:
Starting to Read

Level 3:
Becoming a Reader

Level 4:
Building Confidence

Level 5:
Reading with
Confidence

OXFORD
UNIVERSITY PRESS
Great Clarendon Street,
Oxford OX2 6DP

Text © Roderick Hunt 2006
Illustrations © Alex Brychta 2006

First published 2006
All rights reserved

Series Editors: Kate Ruttle,
Annemarie Young

British Library Cataloguing
in Publication Data available

ISBN–13: 978-019-279232-7

10 9 8 7 6 5 4 3 2

Printed in China by Imago